Recorder Anthology 1

Initial to Grade 1

Accompanied & solo pieces
for descant & treble recorder

Contents

Published by
Trinity College London
Registered Office:
89 Albert Embankment
London SE1 7TP UK

T +44 (0)20 7820 6100
F +44 (0)20 7820 6161
E music@trinitycollege.co.uk
www.trinitycollege.co.uk

Registered in the UK
Company no. 02683033
Charity no. 1014792

Copyright © 2011 Trinity College London
Second impression, June 2013

Layout: Catherine Duffy

Printed in England by Halstan & Co. Ltd, Amersham, Bucks.

Descant

Bransle des Cheveaux

Arranged by
Otto Proctor

Thoinot Arbeau
(1520-1595)

Moderato [♩ = 112]

Descant
unaccompanied

Deep Blue C

Otto Proctor

[♩ = 120–136]

Descant

Rigaudon

Arranged by
Peter Robinson

Henry Purcell
(1659-1695)

Allegretto [♩ = 96]

Descant

Echo

Edgar Hunt

Andante ♩ = 108

Recorder 1 Anthology

Initial to Grade 1

Accompanied & solo pieces
for descant & treble recorder

Piano accompaniment

Emily !!!

Published by
Trinity College London

Registered Office:
89 Albert Embankment
London SE1 7TP UK

T +44 (0)20 7820 6100
F +44 (0)20 7820 6161
E music@trinitycollege.co.uk
www.trinitycollege.co.uk

Registered in the UK
Company no. 02683033
Charity no. 1014792

Layout: Catherine Duffy

Printed in England by Halstan & Co. Ltd, Amersham, Bucks.

Contents

Bransle des Cheveaux

Arranged by Otto Proctor

Thoinot Arbeau
(1520-1595)

Moderato [♩ = 112]

Descant

Rigaudon

Arranged by
Peter Robinson

Henry Purcell
(1659-1695)

Allegretto [♩ = 96]

5

Descant

Echo

Edgar Hunt

Descant

Turn the Glasses Over

Accompaniment by
Robin Hagues

Traditional

Descant

Rigaudon

Joseph Bodin de Boismortier
(1689-1755)

Descant

Home Sweet Home

Accompaniment by
Robin Hagues

Traditional

9

Descant or Treble

O Jesulein, süss

Melody by Samuel Scheidt (1587-1654)

Harmonisation by Johann Sebastian Bach (1685-1750)

Andante sostenuto [♩ = 96]

O Jesulein, süss = O Jesus so sweet

His Rest

Giles Farnaby
(c. 1563-1640)

First March for the Rustic Wedding

Jean Hotteterre
(*d.* 1720)

Descant

Since First I Saw Thy Face

from *Musicke of Sundrie Kindes*, 1607

Transcribed from the lute
tablature by Edgar Hunt

Thomas Ford

Descant

Under the Greenwood Tree

Arranged by
David Wright

Traditional

15

Descant or Treble

Honiesuckle

Edited by
Peter Robinson

Anthony Holborne
(*d*. 1602)

Descant

Fairest Isle

Arranged by
David Wright

Henry Purcell
(1659-1695)

18

Descant

Passetyme with gude companye

Edited by
Peter Robinson

Henry VIII

19

Descant or Treble
unaccompanied

Study no. 8

J H Feltkamp

Descant

Turn the Glasses Over

Accompaniment by
Robin Hagues

Traditional

Descant

Rigaudon

Joseph Bodin de Boismortier
(1689-1755)

Moderato [♩ = 72]

© Copyright 1997 Trinity College London

Descant

Home Sweet Home

Accompaniment by
Robin Hagues

Traditional

Moderato [♩ = 108]

6

O Jesulein, süss

Melody by Samuel Scheidt (1587-1654)
Harmonisation by Johann Sebastian Bach (1685-1750)

O Jesulein, süss = O Jesus so sweet

Descant
unaccompanied

Ländler

Austrian folk dance

Anon.

His Rest

Giles Farnaby
(c. 1563-1640)

[♩ = 108]

Descant or Treble
unaccompanied

Branle

from *Danserye*, pub. 1551

Tylman Susato
(c. 1500-1562)

Allegro [♩ = 72]

Descant or Treble

First March for the Rustic Wedding

Jean Hotteterre
(*d.* 1720)

Descant

Since First I Saw Thy Face

from *Musicke of Sundrie Kindes*, 1607

Transcribed from the lute
tablature by Edgar Hunt

Thomas Ford

Descant

Under the Greenwood Tree

Arranged by
David Wright

Traditional

Descant or Treble

Honiesuckle

Edited by
Peter Robinson

Anthony Holborne
(*d.* 1602)

10

Descant
unaccompanied

Galopede

Anon.

Descant

Fairest Isle

Arranged by
David Wright

Henry Purcell
(1659-1695)

Passetyme with gude companye

Edited by
Peter Robinson

Henry VIII

Treble
unaccompanied

Tune for a Starling

from *The Bird Fancyer's Delight*, 1717

Edited by
Peter Robinson

Anon.